Time Pieces

for
Clarinet

Music through the Ages in Three Volumes

Volume 3

Ian Denley

The Associated Board of
the Royal Schools of Music

CONTENTS

Time Pieces for Clarinet

Volume 3

for Sharon

c.1722 Sarabande
from Suite in E Flat, BWV 819/3

Johann Sebastian Bach
(1685–1750)

AB 2676

1791 Adagio für Glasharmonika

K. 356

Wolfgang Amadeus Mozart
(1756–1791)

Adagio semplice e con molto espressione ($\quad = c.60$)

Clarinet in B♭

Piano

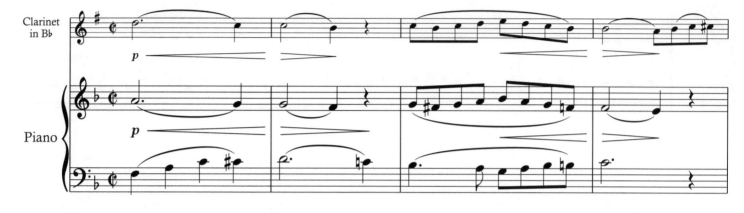

AB 2676

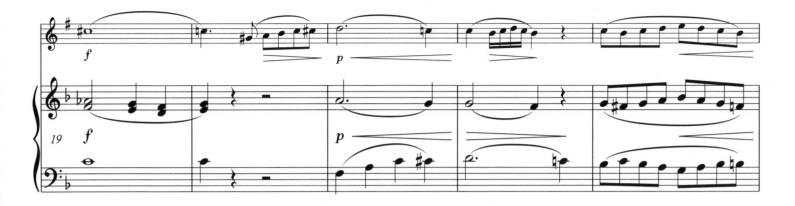

1831 Menuetto e Trio

from Sonata in B Flat, Op. 1

Richard Wagner
(1813–1883)

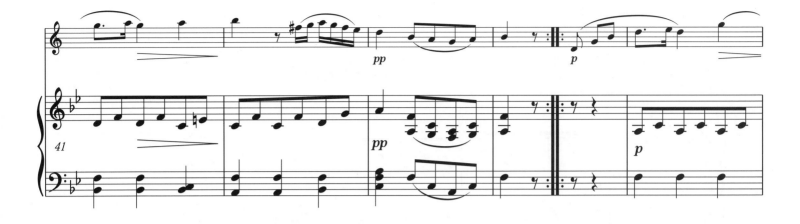

Menuetto D.C. e poi Coda – Repeat the Menuetto, and then play the Coda

***Menuetto D.C.
e poi Coda****

Ballade

Op. 100 No. 15

Johann Burgmüller
(1806–1874)

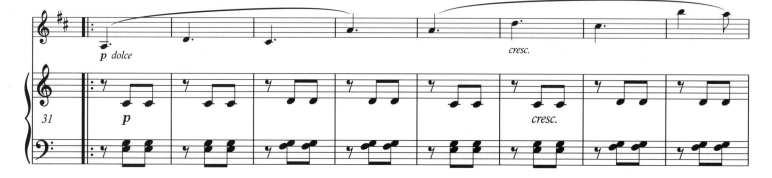

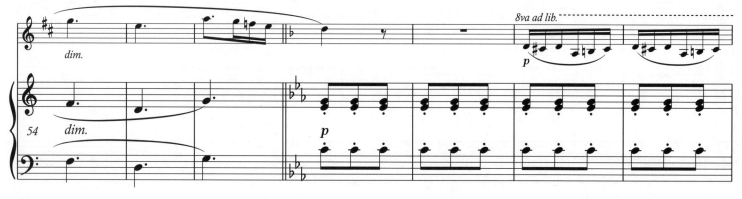

1872 Andante cantabile

from Quartet in D, Op. 11

Pyotr Tchaikovsky
(1840–1893)

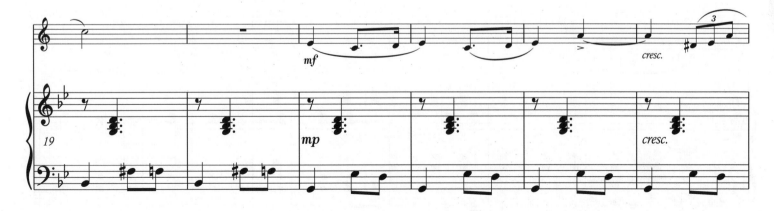

AB 2676

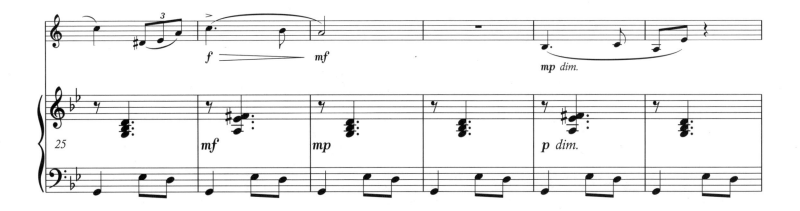

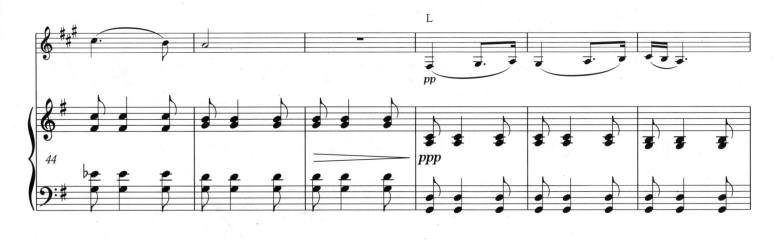

L

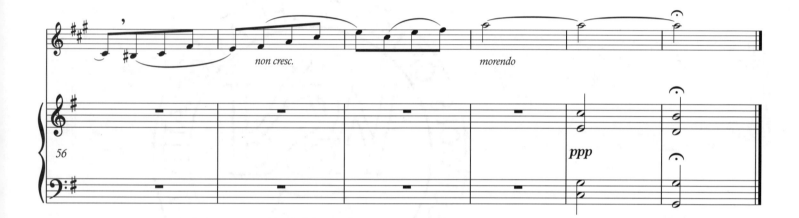

non cresc.   morendo

ppp

1897 **Du meines Herzens Krönelein**

Richard Strauss
(1864–1949)

(You, the crown of my heart)

from *Schlichte Weisen*, Op. 21

Andante (♩ = c.84)

[pochiss. rit.]   [a tempo]

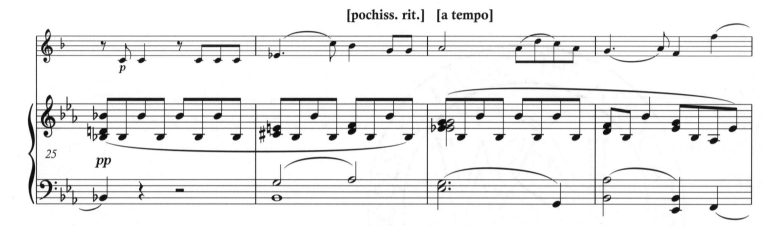

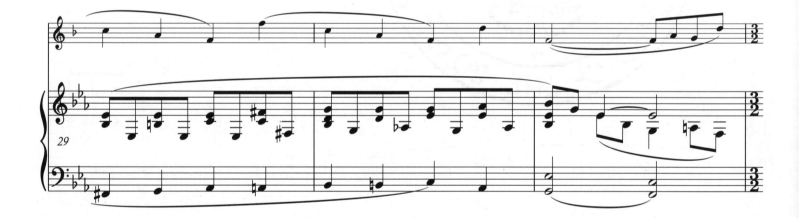

rit.

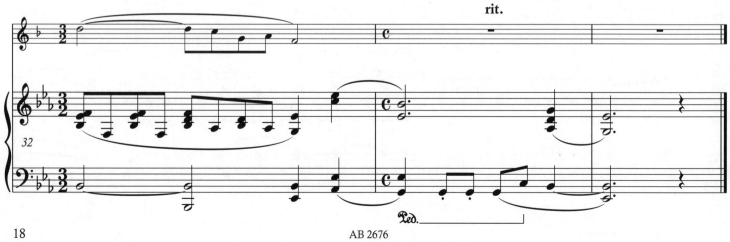

1900 Fast zu keck

(Almost too cheeky)

Max Reger
(1873–1916)

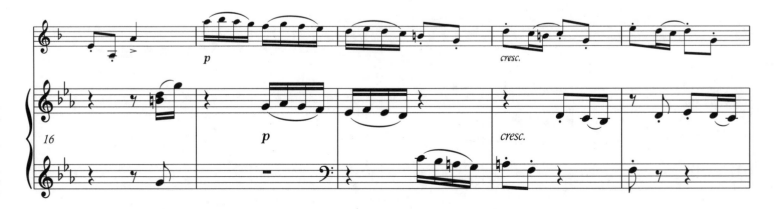

AB 2676

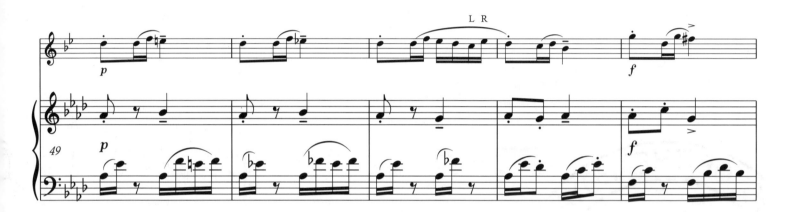

D.C. al Fine

1907   **Menuett in F**

Alban Berg
(1885–1935)

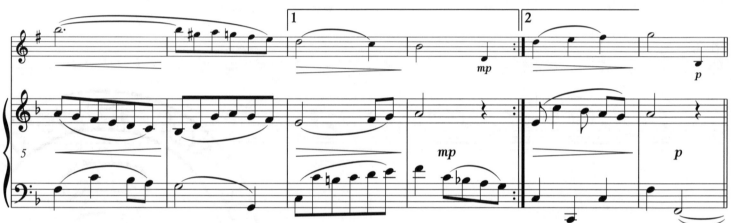

1908 Solo

from Symphony No. 2, Op. 27

Serge Rachmaninov
(1873–1943)

Adagio (♩ = c.50)

Clarinet in B♭

Piano

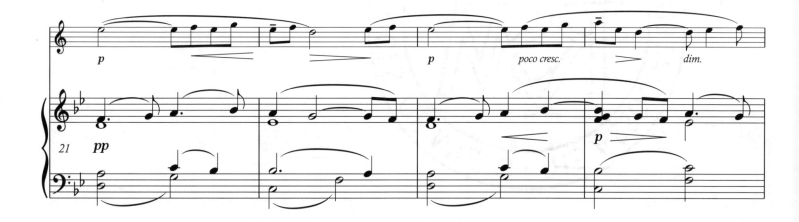

March

from *Music for Children*, Op. 65 No. 10

Serge Prokofiev
(1891–1953)

Tempo di marcia (♩ = *c*.120)

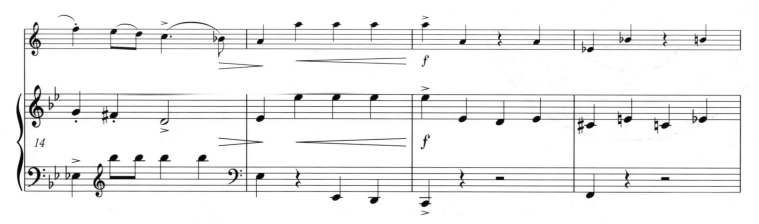

1951 # Siciliano

from *Reihe Kleiner Klavierstücke*

Henk Badings
(1907–1987)

1967 Fable No. 9

from *Fables*, Op. 21

Robert Muczynski

(b. 1929)

allargando

1972 Les Jeux de Guillaume

(William's Games)

from *Gestes et Sentiments*

Georges Friboulet
(b. 1910)

Moderato (assez décidé *) ($\quad$ = *c*.66–72)

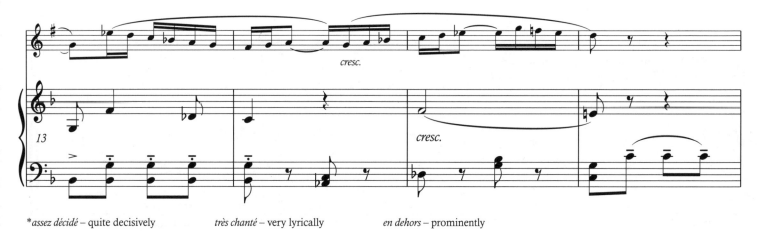

*assez décidé – quite decisively   *très chanté* – very lyrically   *en dehors* – prominently

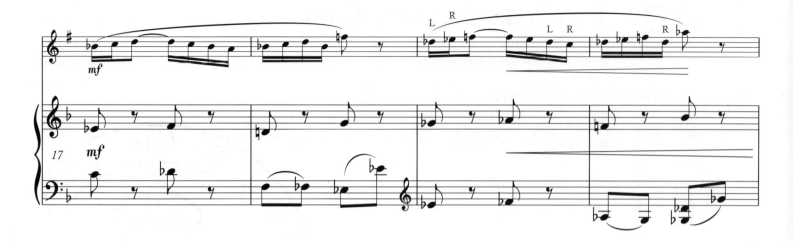

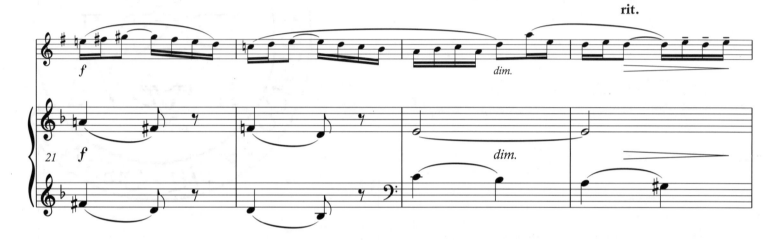

AB 2676

Music origination by
Barnes Music Engraving Ltd, East Sussex
Printed in England by Caligraving Ltd, Thetford, Norfolk

10:06